Michael
Herczeg

INFLUENCING SOCIETY

God's Design for the Family

BOOK 4

NAVPRESS

A MINISTRY OF THE NAVIGATORS

P.O. Box 20, Colorado Springs, Colorado 80901

The Navigators is an international, evangelical Christian
organization. Jesus Christ gave
His followers the Great Commission to go and make disciples
(Matthew 28:19). The aim of The
Navigators is to help fulfill that
commission by multiplying
laborers for Christ in every
nation.

NavPress is the publishing
ministry of The Navigators.
NavPress publications are tools
to help Christians grow.
Although publications alone cannot make disciples or change
lives, they can help believers
learn biblical discipleship, and
apply what they learn to their
lives and ministries.

Scripture quotations are from
the *New International Version,*
© 1978 by the New York International Bible Society.

Printed in the United States of
   America

CONTENTS

IN RECOGNITION

These staff members of The Navigators made the major contribution to the prayerful and thoughtful preparation of *God's Design for the Family:* Rod Beidler, Bruce Das, Ray Hoo, Doug Prensner, Ed Reis, Gene Soderberg, and Bob Sparks. The aim of the series has been to provide married couples with biblical principles and patterns that lead to dynamic family growth in love, and to harmony in their relationships with God and their families.

In addition, appreciation is due to the wives of the staff members, who provided help and ideas as the project developed; to other Navigator staff members who participated in various stages of planning and preparing the series; and to a large number of staff, pastors, and lay men and women who field-tested the manuscripts.

BEFORE YOU BEGIN

These studies are written for use by married couples, or by singles planning to be married. Both partners should answer the questions separately, and then discuss them with each other. You will gain even more benefit by meeting regularly with other couples after all of you have answered the questions. The recommended pace is one chapter per week, with a group discussion time for each chapter. Group discussion guidelines for all the chapters are included in this book, beginning on page 77.

Each chapter includes application questions and suggested family project ideas to help you apply to your family life the things you are learning in your study. Before deciding on each application, remember to pray about it. God knows the needs in your life which He wants you to work on now. Stay in communication with Him as you plan, and be confident that He will lead you. Pray also for insight and strength in putting your applications into practice.

CHAPTER 1

THE CHURCH AND THE FAMILY

IN the Church the world can see whether Christianity really works. When Christians follow biblical principles for true fellowship, their love for each other, their holy lifestyle, and their unified evangelistic outreach will serve as a strong witness to the world, as well as a forceful example for our children.

Francis Schaeffer wrote, "In the name of our Lord Jesus Christ we are called upon to show to a watching world and to our own young people that the Church is something beautiful."*

THE CHURCH— GOD'S FAMILY

1. Read Colossians 1:18 (which describes Jesus Christ), and then Acts 13:1. How is the word *church* used differently in these two passages?

_____

_____

_____

_____

*Francis Schaeffer, *The Church Before the Watching World* (Downers Grove, Illinos: InterVarsity Press, 1971), page 63.

9

2. Read Mark 3:31-35. From Jesus' teaching in this passage, who would you say are members of Christ's family?

_____

_____

_____

3. How is Christ's Church described in Romans 12:4-5?

_____

_____

_____

_____

4. Paul taught much about the Church as the Body of Christ in 1 Corinthians 12. Read verses 14-27 of this chapter, and summarize three or four major points of the passage.

_____

_____

_____

_____

_____

_____

_____

_____

_____

5. List two persons in your local church who you and your family depend on in an important way in some aspect of your lives, and describe what need they fill.

_____

_____

_____

_____

_____

_____

_____

6. From Ephesians 4:11-16, explain why Christians have different functions in the Body of Christ.

_____

_____

_____

_____

_____

_____

7. From the following passages, list some of the benefits we receive from the Body of Christ by following biblical principles.

Romans 12:13_____

_____

_____

Romans 15:7_____

_____

_____

2 Corinthians 1:3-4_____

_____

_____

11

Galatians 6:2 _____

_____

_____

1 Thessalonians 5:14 _____

_____

_____

James 5:14-16 _____

_____

_____

1 Peter 4:8-9 _____

_____

_____

1 John 3:16-18 _____

_____

_____

List any example of how another Christian has
served you or your family in one of the ways
described in these passages.

_____

_____

_____

_____

_____

CONTRIBUTING TO GOD'S FAMILY

8. From these passages, explain how we should
   relate to spiritual leaders:

1 Thessalonians 5:12-13 _____

_____

_____

Hebrews 13:17 _____

_____

_____

9. According to these passages, who should we give
to financially?

Proverbs 19:17 _____

Galatians 6:6 _____

10. What other contributions that we can make to the
Church are mentioned in these passages:

Colossians 3:16 _____

_____

_____

1 Timothy 5:3 _____

_____

_____

1 Peter 4:10-11 _____

_____

_____

11. How can you and your family use your gifts, time,
possessions, finances, or your home to supply
some needs of others?

_____

_____

_____

_____

13

THE MEANING
OF FELLOWSHIP

12. Write in your own words a definition of true
    Christian fellowship, perhaps using a dictionary or
    Bible dictionary to help you.

    _____

    _____

    _____

    _____

    _____

    _____

    _____

13. How was Christian fellowship demonstrated in
    these passages from Acts:

    2:44-47 _____

    _____

    _____

    _____

    _____

    4:23-24 _____

    _____

    _____

    _____

    12:5-12 _____

    _____

    _____

    _____

13:1-3 _____

_____

_____

_____

14. Meditate on these passages, and tell what aspect of fellowship is contained in each one:

Galatians 6:9-10 _____

_____

_____

Ephesians 6:18 _____

_____

_____

Philippians 1:27 _____

_____

_____

Hebrews 3:12-13 _____

_____

_____

Which of these is most important to your family in your fellowship with other Christians?

_____

_____

_____

_____

_____

15. What hindrances to true fellowship are described in the passages on the next page?

Acts 5:1-11 _____

_____

_____

1 Corinthians 1:10-12 _____

_____

_____

Philippians 2:21 _____

_____

_____

James 2:1-4 _____

_____

_____

James 2:14-17 _____

_____

_____

16. Can you think of anything which tends to hinder
your family's experience of true fellowship with
other Christians? If so, how can you overcome
this?

_____

_____

_____

_____

_____

A MODEL
CHURCH

17. Read 1 Thessalonians 1:3. What did Paul particularly commend the Thessalonian believers for?

_____

_____

_____

_____

18. From 1 Thessalonians 1:6-7, how did the Thessalonians respond to Paul's ministry?

_____

_____

_____

19. Every local church can contribute to God's worldwide mission. From 1 Thessalonians 1:8-10, how would you describe the impact of the church at Thessalonica?

_____

_____

_____

20. Read 1 Thessalonians 2:13. What attitude toward God's Word characterized this church?

_____

_____

_____

21. Paul sent Timothy to Thessalonica to minister to the church there. When Timothy returned, he brought to Paul good news about two aspects of the Christian life of those in the church (1 Thessalonians 3:6). What were these two aspects?

_____

_____

_____

17

Would a newcomer to your church be impressed with these two qualities? Explain your answer.

_____

_____

_____

_____

_____

_____

_____

THE CHURCH'S IMPACT ON THE WORLD

22. Explain in your own words what Jesus taught in these two passages about how His disciples can influence the world:

    John 13:34-35 _____

    _____

    _____

    John 17:20-21 _____

    _____

    _____

23. What did Jesus promise about the Church in Matthew 16:18?

    _____

    _____

    _____

    _____

18

24. What purposes for the Church are given in these passages?

Hebrews 10:24-25 _____

_____

_____

1 Peter 2:9-10 _____

_____

_____

What do you think is the best way your family can be involved in these purposes for the Church?

_____

_____

_____

_____

_____

_____

HOW TO CONTRIBUTE TO YOUR CHURCH

1. Take written notes during the pastor's sermon and in Sunday school classes and discussions.
2. During family devotions or around the dinner table, have each family member tell something that was particularly helpful to him from the worship service or from a Sunday school class the previous Sunday.
3. Open your home to provide meals and lodging to visiting missionaries and other church guests.
4. Remember to always speak positively at home about your pastor, church leaders, and others in the church.
5. Prayerfully accept responsibilities, and do them well.

APPLICATION

(In the application section at the end of each chapter you may find it helpful to discuss what you have written with your spouse, and perhaps with others in your family.)

25. Write a brief statement of what you believe are the two or three major reasons the Church is important to you and your family.

_____

_____

_____

_____

_____

_____

_____

_____

26. Prayerfully review your answers in this chapter. Record here any specific ways in which you are convinced you and your family should work to improve your relationship with your local church or other Christians.

_____

_____

_____

_____

_____

_____

How and when will you put this into action?

_____

_____

_____

SUGGESTED FAMILY PROJECTS

(These projects, and those listed at the end of later chapters, can be a valuable exercise for practicing the scriptural principles you have studied in this chapter. As you read the instructions for the projects, think of creative ways to make them meaningful and enjoyable for each member of your family. Plan to include every child who is old enough to enjoy the time with you. If your children are older, allow time for deeper discussion of thoughts and questions they may have, and let them help you plan the project.)

a. Have a discussion around the dinner table on this question: "Why does our family *need* the Church?" (Try to get answers from each family member. You can record their answers here.)

_____

_____

_____

_____

_____

_____

_____

_____

_____

b. Make a list of the ways in which your family is involved in your local church. Then, on the line scale below, mark where your family is, in your opinion, in the extent of your church involvement. Be sure to record the opinions of your spouse and your children.

_____

_____

_____

_____

_____

_____

_____

_____

_____

Underinvolved   Overinvolved

└_____┘

If your marks are on the underinvolved side, list possible needs in the church that your family could help fill.

_____

_____

_____

_____

Who is the appropriate person in your church to contact about helping fill this need, and when will you contact him?

_____

_____

If your family is overinvolved, consider all the activities and responsibilities you now have. Which are the most important?

_____

_____

_____

_____

_____

Which could be dropped or given to others in order to allow you to do a better job in your most important responsibilities, and to spend more time together as a family? (Remember that relinquishing some responsibilities can provide important opportunities for others to increase their involvement.)

_____

_____

_____

_____

_____

CHAPTER 2

INFLUENCING NON-CHRISTIANS

TO many, she might have seemed an unlikely candidate for believing in Christ. But in a conversation of love and truth at Jacob's well, Jesus convinced the Samaritan woman of His identity. Afterwards He told His disciples that such opportunities for influencing people are abundant: "I tell you, open your eyes and look at the fields! They are ripe for harvest" (John 4:35). The same is true today.

SALT, LIGHT, AND FRAGRANCE

1. Read Matthew 5:13-16. In verse 13, Jesus called His followers "the salt of the earth." What are some characteristics of salt?

_____

_____

_____

_____

_____

Write down on the next page what you think Jesus meant by using the term "salt of the earth" to describe His followers.

25

_____
_____
_____
_____
_____
_____

2. Compare Matthew 5:13 with Luke 14:25-35. How can a Christian family lose its "saltiness"?

_____
_____
_____
_____

3. Look again at Matthew 5:14-16. Why do you think *light* is a good word to describe the influence Christians can have in the world?

_____
_____
_____
_____
_____

4. What can you learn from these passages about some ways a Christian family could hide its light?

Philippians 2:14-15_____

_____
_____

1 Peter 2:11-12_____

_____

_____

_____

5. Write a brief statement about how you think your family can best allow its light to penetrate the darkness of the non-Christian world.

_____

_____

_____

_____

_____

_____

_____

6. Jesus commanded His followers to let their light shine before men "that they may see your good deeds and praise your Father in heaven" (Matthew 5:16). How do you think non-Christians can praise and glorify God as a result of seeing our good deeds?

_____

_____

_____

_____

_____

_____

7. How can we make sure that other people praise

God for the good deeds they see in our lives,
rather than giving all the glory to us?

_____

_____

_____

_____

_____

8. Read 2 Corinthians 2:14-17, in which Paul por-
   trayed the influence Christians have in society.
   Then rephrase verses 15 and 16 in your own
   words, perhaps stating them as they relate to
   how your own family can influence the world.

_____

_____

_____

_____

_____

_____

_____

9. According to 2 Corinthians 2:14, who actually
   spreads the fragrance of Christ?

_____

10. In what ways are the influence of salt, light, and
    fragrance alike?

_____

_____

_____

_____

11. What one or two things in your answers to Questions 1-10 are most meaningful to you regarding your family's influence in society?

_____

_____

_____

_____

_____

_____

_____

Salt must be placed on the food before it can season it; light must be dispersed before it penetrates darkness; and fragrance is useless unless it is where it can be detected. In the same way, the Christian family must be involved in the world in order to influence it.

JESUS' EXAMPLE

12. Study Luke 5:27-32. What kind of people did Jesus associate with in this instance?

_____

_____

_____

How did the Pharisees and the scribes (teachers of the law) react to Jesus' behavior?

_____

_____

_____

_____

State in your own words the reply Jesus gave to their objections.

_____

_____

_____

_____

_____

13. Read Matthew 11:19. Jesus was looked down on by some because of His association with sinners. To what extent do you think you should be willing to take this risk?

_____

_____

_____

_____

In what ways can your family follow Jesus' example in relating to non-Christians?

_____

_____

_____

_____

_____

BEING IN
THE WORLD

14. Study 1 Corinthians 9:19-23. What basic attitude did Paul have in his relationships with non-Christians?

30

_____

_____

_____

_____

What were his reasons for having this attitude?

_____

_____

_____

_____

_____

_____

15. What danger did Paul warn about in Galatians 5:13?

_____

_____

How would you say this applies to our involvement with non-Christians?

_____

_____

_____

_____

_____

16. Read Jesus' prayer for His disciples in John 17:6-19. In verse 15 He said His prayer was not that God would take the disciples out of the world,

but that He would protect them from the evil one. List at least three other requests Jesus made for His disciples in this prayer.

_____

_____

_____

_____

_____

_____

_____

_____

_____

_____

17. In John 17:14, how did Jesus describe the unique position held by His disciples?

_____

_____

_____

Explain briefly what this means for you and your family.

_____

_____

_____

_____

APPLICATION

18. Prayerfully review your answers in this chapter. Why do you personally believe it is important for

you and your family to be involved in some way
with non-Christians?

_____

_____

_____

_____

_____

_____

19. Make a list of possible ways your family can get
more involved with non-Christians—such as activities with other families, joining various groups
or organizations, and helping your neighbors in
practical ways. (Don't hesitate to get involved
with individuals who seem to have little interest in
Christianity, as well as those who have shown
interest.)

_____

_____

_____

_____

_____

_____

From this list, what specific action do you believe
you should take at this time?

_____

_____

_____

_____

SUGGESTED
FAMILY
PROJECT

Read together Matthew 5:13-16. Ask each person to
tell how he can be salt and light in his world—in
school, at work, or in the neighborhood. Also talk
about how your family together can influence non-
Christians.

CHAPTER 3

VALUES AND CONDUCT

THE Christian family's basic values and conduct should be distinctive—based on God's eternal Word, and not on man-made traditions, contemporary philosophies, or popular social trends or movements.

SERVING

1. Read Mark 10:42-45. In your own words, what did Jesus say here about how leadership is normally practiced in the world?

   _____

   _____

   _____

   _____

   How did He say His followers should practice leadership?

   _____

   _____

   _____

   _____

2. What do these passages say about serving?

Matthew 25:35-40 _____

_____

_____

_____

_____

John 12:26 _____

_____

_____

John 13:12-15 _____

_____

_____

_____

3. What do you believe are the most important ways you can serve your family?

_____

_____

_____

_____

_____

_____

_____

PRIORITIES

4. Read Matthew 6:25-34. What should be the Christian family's first priority? (verse 33)

_____

_____

_____

_____

What things can compete for our first loyalty?
(verses 31-32)

_____

_____

_____

_____

5. Read Luke 8:14. List the things mentioned that
   can keep the Word of God from bearing fruit in
   your family's life.

_____

_____

_____

6. Read Philippians 4:6-7. How should we handle the
   worries of life?

_____

_____

_____

7. God has made the family our most important
   social unit. How do the following passages tell of
   the importance of the family in God's eyes?

   Matthew 19:4-6_____

   _____

   _____

1 Timothy 3:2-5_____

_____

_____

1 Timothy 5:8_____

_____

_____

Titus 2:3-5_____

_____

_____

8. Read Matthew 10:37-38. How should the family compare in priority with your relationship to Jesus?

_____

_____

_____

_____

PRIORITIES

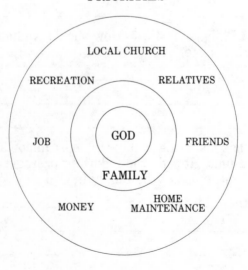

9. Take a few minutes to analyze the priority you give to your family. Are you giving it the same importance God does?

_____

_____

_____

_____

If not, what steps do you believe you should take to change the situation?

_____

_____

_____

_____

_____

POSSESSIONS

10. From each of these passages in 1 Timothy 6, tell what should be a Christian family's attitudes toward possessions.

Verses 6-8_____

_____

_____

Verse 17_____

_____

_____

Verses 18-19_____

_____

_____

11. Generosity is an antidote to the poison of the love
of money. What dangers are associated with the
love of money? (1 Timothy 6:9-10)

_____

_____

_____

_____

_____

BEING HOSPITABLE

12. Using a dictionary, write out a definition of
    hospitality.

_____

_____

_____

_____

_____

13. Read Romans 12:13, then paraphrase it, using the
    definition you wrote above.

_____

_____

_____

_____

_____

14. What reason is given in Hebrews 13:2 for being
    hospitable?

_____

_____

_____

_____

15. Read Genesis 18:1-8. Describe how Abraham and Sarah treated their three visitors.

_____

_____

_____

_____

Who were these men?

_____

_____

16. What reasons for hospitality did God give to Israel in Leviticus 19:33-34?

_____

_____

_____

How could this example be applied to your relationship to families who have just moved into your neighborhood?

_____

_____

_____

_____

What practical things could you do to help ease
the adjustments that new neighbors must make?

_____

_____

_____

_____

_____

_____

17. Read 1 Peter 4:9. What attitude should
    characterize our hospitality?

_____

_____

18. In Acts 17:1-9 we read how being hospitable was
    costly to a Christian named Jason in Thessalonica,
    where Paul had come to preach the Gospel. What
    happened to Jason?

_____

_____

_____

THE IMPORTANCE
OF GOD'S WORD

19. Paul mentioned four things in 2 Timothy 3:16 for
    which the Scriptures are useful or profitable. List
    ways in which each of these can affect your
    family's lifestyle.

_____

_____

_____

_____

_____

_____

_____

_____

_____

_____

_____

20. Read John 14:21. What is one result of having and obeying God's commandments?

_____

_____

WAYS YOUR FAMILY CAN LEARN MORE FROM GOD'S WORD
1. Have frequent devotional times together, centered around a passage of Scripture. 2. Have everyone involved in regular Scripture memory—and set an example for them by meditating on and applying the verses you learn. 3. Use mealtimes and other times together to discuss scriptural principles and commands that relate to current needs and circumstances in your family. 4. Make sure each child has a Bible version he can read and understand on his own, and write in.

APPLICATION

21. Prayerfully review your answers in this chapter. List on the next page the things you learned which are most meaningful to you.

_____
_____
_____
_____
_____
_____
_____

Related to what you listed above, describe any
need in your life that you believe you should work
on at this time.

_____
_____
_____
_____

What passage of Scripture in this chapter relates
to this need?

_____
_____
_____

What specific action will you take?

_____
_____
_____
_____

How will you evaluate your progress?

_____
_____

SUGGESTED
FAMILY
PROJECT

Read together Romans 12:9-21. This passage contains many principles for Christian conduct. Discuss the passage together, then list about four of these principles which are important to your family at this time. Then write down what you think are the opposites to these principles (as in the example below). Decide on ways you can carry out the principles and avoid doing their opposites. (Use the spaces below, or your own paper or chalkboard.)

CHRISTIAN PRINCIPLE	ITS OPPOSITE
Sincere love	Pretended love

WHAT OUR FAMILY WILL DO

45

CHAPTER 4

THE FAMILY AND WORK

TO many people, work is only a necessary evil. Even some Christians chafe under the restrictions of their jobs, and think that their work keeps them from serving God enough. But the Scriptures tell how important work is—and how fulfilling it can be when done for the Lord.

OLD TESTAMENT PRINCIPLES AND EXAMPLES

1. Read Genesis 2:15. For what purpose did God place Adam in the Garden of Eden?

   _____

   _____

   _____

   _____

2. Read Genesis 3:17-19. After man's fall into sin, what did God say man's work would be like?

   _____

   _____

   _____

3. What evidence do these passages give that work was a normal part of life in the Old Testament?

Psalm 104:21-23 _____

_____

Psalm 90:17 _____

_____

Ruth 2:2-3 _____

_____

Leviticus 26:3-5 _____

_____

_____

4. Read Exodus 20:8-11. What are the two major parts of this commandment?

Verse 9 _____

_____

Verse 10 _____

_____

The Christian can be equally obeying God when he "clocks in" at work or works at home, and when he worships God.

5. Proverbs 31:10-31 describes a wife of noble character, and commends her work. What are at least five jobs in which she was involved?

_____

_____

_____

_____

_____

_____

_____

_____

_____

What were the results of her hard work? (verses 28-31)

_____

_____

_____

_____

_____

How do you think this passage can be applied to your family?

_____

_____

_____

_____

_____

6. The last chapters of Exodus recount the making of the Tabernacle after the Hebrews left Egypt.

Read Exodus 35:30—36:1. How did God prepare Bezalel and Oholiab for the jobs they were given?

_____

_____

_____

_____

_____

_____

_____

7. Read Joshua 1:1-6. What job was Joshua given?

_____

_____

_____

8. Read Joshua 11:15. How well did Joshua carry out his responsibilities?

_____

_____

_____

9. Read Jeremiah 1:4-10. Who appointed Jeremiah to be a prophet to the nations?

_____

What was his task? (Jeremiah 1:7)

_____

_____

_____

10. Daniel was among the people of Judah who were exiled to Babylon. Read Daniel 2:48-49 and 5:29. What responsibilities did God provide for Daniel in Babylon?

_____

_____

_____

_____

_____

11. Read Isaiah 28:23-29. Who is the source of the farmer's effectiveness?

   _____

12. Read Psalm 111:2. How do you think God is working now? (See also John 5:17 and Acts 13:41.)

   _____

   _____

   _____

   _____

   _____

   _____

NEW TESTAMENT PRINCIPLES AND EXAMPLES

13. Read Mark 6:1-3. What had been Jesus' occupation before beginning His final three years of ministry?

   _____

14. Read Mark 7:37. What observation did the people make in this instance about how Jesus conducted His ministry?

   _____

   _____

15. What principle about work did Jesus give in
Luke 10:7?

_____

_____

_____

16. How did Jesus describe His earthly ministry in
John 4:34 and 17:4?

_____

_____

_____

_____

17. Read Acts 18:3. What was Paul's trade?

_____

18. Read 1 Corinthians 7:17-24. How does Paul's
teaching here relate to job satisfaction?

_____

_____

_____

_____

19. What reasons for his own hard work did Paul give
in 2 Thessalonians 3:6-9?

_____

_____

_____

_____

_____

20. What did Paul teach in 2 Thessalonians 3:10-12 as reasons for working?

_____

_____

_____

_____

_____

_____

21. What other reason for working did Paul give in Ephesians 4:28?

_____

_____

_____

22. Read Colossians 3:22-24. What was Paul's teaching to slaves about work?

_____

_____

_____

_____

_____

How could you apply this passage to the way you do your work?

_____

_____

_____

23. What instructions did Paul give to slaves in 1 Timothy 6:1-2?

_____

_____

_____

_____

How do you think this passage applies to your work?

_____

_____

"In the experience of grace, human tasks are given a new value and become more worthwhile. They are performed for the sake of the Name. And in their fulfillment in this context they are thrice blessed. The one who works is himself blessed in his reception of divine grace to carry through his labors for the glory of God; those who receive the results of such tasks done in a new spirit and with a new quality are benefited also; and in all God is Himself glorified."

—H.D. McDonald*

24. Read Jesus' parable of the rich fool in Luke 12:13-21. How do you think this parable should apply to our attitude toward possessions and our purpose for working?

_____

_____

_____

_____

_____

*The New Bible Dictionary (Grand Rapids, Michigan: Wm. B. Eerdmans Publishing Co., 1962), page 1338.

APPLICATION

25. Prayerfully review your answers in this chapter. Summarize here the principles you learned which most impressed you.

_____

_____

_____

_____

_____

_____

_____

26. Record here any need in your life pertaining to work that you believe you should work on at this time.

_____

_____

_____

What passage of Scripture in this chapter relates to this need?

_____

_____

_____

What specific action will you take?

_____

_____

_____

How will you evaluate your progress?

_____

_____

SUGGESTED FAMILY PROJECT

Read together Exodus 20:8-11, and talk about what it means for each member of your family to work six days and to rest on the seventh. How do you rest? Does everyone in your family understand the biblical view of work and rest? Are all family members finding fulfillment in their jobs? Discuss ways to experience greater levels of satisfaction through work, and how to better balance work with adequate rest and recreation. One suggestion: At breakfast together Monday morning, or perhaps sometime on Sunday, pray together about each person's work and school responsibilities in the coming week.

CHAPTER 5

REACHING OUT

GOD wants the blessings He bestows on His people to be passed on to all the world's peoples. Abraham was promised, "All peoples on earth will be blessed through you" (Genesis 12:3). Through the Prophet Isaiah, the Lord said to His servant, "It is too small a thing for you to be My servant to restore the tribes of Jacob and bring back those of Israel I have kept. I will also make you a light for the Gentiles, that you may bring My salvation to the ends of the earth" (Isaiah 49:6). And in His risen glory Jesus commanded His followers to "go and make disciples of all nations" (Matthew 28:19). As the people of God on earth today, this responsibility is now ours.

SENT
BY GOD

1. Read 2 Corinthians 2:12—3:6. What gave Paul his confidence as a messenger of the Gospel?

   _____

   _____

   _____

   _____

   _____

2. Read John 20:21. What did Jesus say to His disciples after His resurrection?

_____

_____

_____

3. Read Romans 10:12-15. Who can experience salvation?

_____

_____

_____

What process is necessary before they can experience salvation?

_____

_____

_____

4. Read Matthew 4:19. How would you define a "fisher of men"?

_____

_____

_____

_____

How does one become a fisher of men?

_____

_____

_____

_____

5. What similarities can you think of between fishing for fish and fishing for men?

_____

_____

_____

_____

_____

_____

6. How do the following passages show that Paul was a fisher of men?

1 Corinthians 2:1-5 _____

_____

_____

_____

_____

2 Corinthians 6:3-10 _____

_____

_____

_____

_____

Philippians 1:12-14 _____

_____

_____

_____

Colossians 1:28-29 _____

_____

_____

_____

7. What requirements for effective witnessing are mentioned in 1 Peter 3:15-16?

_____

_____

_____

_____

_____

How would you define *hope* as it is used in this passage?

_____

_____

_____

_____

_____

Why do you think people would ask us about our hope?

_____

_____

_____

_____

_____

8. Read the account of Paul's imprisonment with Silas in Philippi (Acts 16:19-34). How did Paul and Silas react in this situation to their circumstances? (verse 25)

_____

_____

_____

How did the other prisoners respond to Paul and Silas? (verse 25)

_____

_____

9. Writing from prison, Paul asked the Colossians to pray for him (Colossians 4:3-4). For what two things did he request them to pray?

_____

_____

10. Read Acts 5:42, and record the places mentioned in which they witnessed for Christ.

_____

_____

_____

11. Following the murder of Stephen (Acts 7), a "great persecution" arose against Christians in Jerusalem, and they were scattered throughout the surrounding areas. According to Acts 8:4, what did they do after leaving Jerusalem?

_____

_____

WHO SHOULD WE REACH

12. In Acts 10 is recorded the conversion of Cornelius, a Roman centurion, through the ministry of the Apostle Peter. Read verses 22-29 of this chapter. Where did Peter meet with Cornelius to speak with him?

_____

_____

Who else was there?

_____

_____

Why was it unusual for Peter to be there?

_____

_____

_____

_____

13. When an expert in the Jewish law asked Him,
    "Who is my neighbor?" Jesus answered with the
    parable of the Good Samaritan (Luke 10:30-37).
    Read this parable, and then summarize the main
    point of Jesus' teaching. Who really is your
    neighbor?

_____

_____

_____

_____

_____

_____

_____

_____

_____

_____

_____

Study this passage to find principles for reaching
out to others, and list them on the next page. Try
to find at least three.

_____

_____

_____

_____

_____

_____

_____

_____

_____

How could one of these principles be effectively applied by your family?

_____

_____

_____

_____

14. Read again Luke 10:31-32. Why do you think the priest and the Levite passed by the injured man?

_____

_____

_____

_____

In reaching out to non-Christians, we must ask ourselves, "Are they comfortable in our presence?" We should not be concerned with our own comfort, but with theirs. This will cost us something—as it did the Good Samaritan. But the art of being a true friend to non-Christians is vitally important for us to learn. And we can be friends without compromising our convictions.

15. Perhaps some of your own children have not yet responded in faith to Christ and come to a personal knowledge of Him. What do these passages say about what parents can do at home to influence their children for the Lord?

Psalm 78:5-8 _____

_____

_____

_____

Ephesians 6:4 _____

_____

_____

APPLICATION

16. Prayerfully review your answers in this chapter. Summarize here the things you learned which most impressed you.

_____

_____

_____

_____

_____

_____

_____

17. List the names of any non-Christians who came to your mind as you studied this chapter and as you thought about your responsibility for reaching out with the message of Christ.

_____

_____

_____

_____

_____

What will you do specifically to reach out to them?

_____

_____

_____

_____

_____

SUGGESTED FAMILY PROJECT

Read together Matthew 4:19, and talk about what it means to each of you. Then make a list together of non-Christians you are particularly concerned for, and pray together for their salvation.

CHAPTER 6

OUR MESSAGE

ONCE we recognize a spiritual need in someone's life, and have an opportunity to talk seriously with him—what do we say? Our message is simple: It is about a person—Jesus Christ. He died for us in love and now lives for us, bringing us into God's presence. He is the source of a new life—in this world and forever.

THE SOURCE OF THE MESSAGE

1. According to John 20:30-31, why did John write his Gospel?

   _____

   _____

   _____

2. What did Paul say about the Scriptures in 2 Timothy 3:14-15?

   _____

   _____

   _____

3. Look over these three passages: Luke 24:25-32;
   Acts 8:26-36; and Acts 17:10-12. What do they
   have in common?

   _____

   _____

   _____

   _____

   _____

   _____

4. Read John 16:7-11. What does the Holy Spirit do?

   _____

   _____

   _____

   _____

   _____

   _____

   _____

5. From the passages below, briefly summarize how
   the Bible, the Holy Spirit, and Christians are involved in multiplying believers in Christ.

   The Bible (Psalm 119:130; Hebrews 4:12-13)

   _____

   _____

   _____

   _____

   _____

The Holy Spirit (2 Corinthians 2:12-14; 1 Thessalonians 1:5)

_____

_____

_____

_____

_____

_____

Christians (1 Corinthians 3:5-7; 2 Corinthians 5:18-20)

_____

_____

_____

_____

_____

Difficulty and ineffectiveness result when we forget this division of labor and try to perform the work of the Bible and the Holy Spirit. But we must not neglect our responsibility for sharing the Good News.

6. Read Matthew's acccount of the parable of the soils (Matthew 13:1-9), and Jesus' explanation of the parable (13:18-23). According to these passages, how would you explain what happens when a person has heard God's Word but doesn't understand it?

_____

_____

_____

_____

What is the explanation for someone who at first was very receptive to God's Word, but soon lost interest?

_____

_____

_____

What has happened when someone has received the Word, but shows no evidence of it, and is instead occupied in many worldly pursuits?

_____

_____

_____

_____

One way to help a non-Christian receive and understand God's Word is to go through one of the Gospels with him chapter by chapter, examining it together and discussing his questions. We cannot make a person believe, but we can help him understand the Scriptures.

GOD'S PLAN
OF SALVATION

7. Read 1 Corinthians 15:1-4. What did Paul include as the ingredients of the Gospel?

_____

_____

_____

_____

8. Read 1 Corinthians 15:17-19. Why is Christ's resurrection an important element in the Gospel?

_____

_____

_____

9. The Book of Romans is an explanation of God's plan of salvation. Summarize in your own words what is taught in each of the following verses, then think of an illustration from daily life which could be helpful to a friend in understanding the teaching.

Man's condition—Romans 3:23

Summary_____

_____

_____

_____

Illustration_____

_____

_____

_____

God's justice—Romans 6:23

Summary_____

_____

_____

_____

Illustration_____

_____

_____

_____

71

God's love—Romans 5:8

Summary _____

_____

_____

_____

Illustration _____

_____

_____

_____

Man's response—Romans 10:9-10

Summary _____

_____

_____

Illustration _____

_____

_____

_____

By memorizing these verses in this order, you
have a concise tool for explaining God's plan of
salvation to others.

10. Read Romans 1:16. What power does the Gospel
have?

_____

_____

_____

11. Read 1 Corinthians 1:18-25. What does Paul say

about the response to the Gospel among those who do not believe in Christ?

_____

_____

_____

_____

_____

12. Read 1 Corinthians 2:1-5. How did Paul communicate the Gospel?

_____

_____

_____

13. Read 1 Peter 3:1-2. When a believing wife is married to a non-Christian husband, what does Paul say will win him over?

_____

_____

14. Often we tend to add nonessential elements to the Gospel, or in some way to make it more demanding or complicated. Read Acts 15:1-11. What problems had arisen among the early Christians? (verses 1-2, 5)

_____

_____

_____

_____

_____

73

What was Peter's conclusion about this issue?

_____

_____

_____

_____

15. What nonessential elements do you think we are prone to add to the Gospel today?

_____

_____

_____

_____

16. Read Galatians 2:11-16. Summarize why Paul opposed Peter in this instance.

_____

_____

_____

_____

_____

_____

APPLICATION

17. In what ways could your lifestyle or your family's lifestyle be obscuring the Gospel from your non-Christian friends?

_____
_____
_____
_____
_____
_____

18. What could you do to improve the quality of your family's witness to others?

_____
_____
_____
_____

19. Write here a brief statement of the Gospel.

_____
_____
_____
_____

20. Do you feel prepared to offer a clear explanation of the Gospel to a non-Christian, when the opportunity arises?

_____

If not, what do you believe you should do to be more adequately prepared?

_____
_____
_____
_____

SUGGESTED FAMILY PROJECT

Discuss together and decide on a plan to have each family member learn the verses from Romans in Question 9 (the "Roman Road") as a tool for sharing Christ. You could memorize the verses one or two per week, discussing each verse together and checking up on each other's memorization. Once you have learned all four verses, take turns presenting and explaining the verses to each other as you would to a non-Christian.

GUIDELINES FOR GROUP DISCUSSION

Discussing this book in a group—such as a Sunday school class or a Bible study group—will allow greater understanding of the scriptural principles you study. The format for this is simple: The group members first answer the questions in a chapter individually at home, and then discuss their findings with each other when they meet together, which is usually once a week.

If you are the discussion leader for such a group, the material on the following pages will help you guide the group in an edifying time of fellowship centered on God's Word.

BEFORE
THE DISCUSSION

As the group leader, your most important preparation for each session is prayer. You will want to make your prayer requests personal, of course, but here are some suggestions:

• Pray that everyone in the group will complete the chapter preparation, and will attend this week's discussion. Ask God to allow each of them to feel the freedom to honestly share his thoughts, and to make a significant contribution to the discussion.

• Ask God to give each of you new understanding and practical applications from the Scriptures as you talk. Pray that the unique needs of each person will be met in this way.

• Pray that you, as the leader, will know the Holy Spirit's guidance in exercising patience, acceptance, sensitivity, and wisdom. Pray for an atmosphere of genuine love in the group, with each member being honestly open to learning and change.

• Pray that as a result of your study and discussion, all of you will obey the Lord more closely and will more clearly demonstrate Christ's presence each day in your families.

After prayer, the next most important aspect of your preparation is to be thoroughly familiar with the chapter you're discussing. Make sure you have answered all the questions and have read the leader's material for that chapter.

GETTING UNDER WAY

When your group is together, work toward having a relaxed and open atmosphere. This may not come quickly, so be especially friendly at first, and communicate to the group that all of you are learning together.

As the leader, take charge in an inoffensive way. The group is looking to you for leadership and you should provide it.

You may want to experiment with various methods for discussing the study material. One simple approach is to discuss it question by question. You can go around the group in order, with the first person giving his answer to Question 1 (followed by a little discussion), the second person answering Question 2, and so on. Or, anyone in the group could answer each question as you come to it (the leader saying something such as "Who would like to take Question 5 for us?"). The question-by-question approach can be a good way to get young Christians started in Bible study discussion. The obvious structure gives them a sense of confidence, and they can see where the discussion is going.

Another method is to lead with a section-by-section

approach. This can provide more spontaneity. Start by asking the group for its impressions of the first section in the chapter you are studying (something like, "What impressed you most from this first section on prayer?"). Remember to direct your question to the entire group, rather than to a certain person.

Someone will then give an answer, probably by referring to a specific question in that section. You can have others share their answers, and then, to discuss the question more thoroughly, ask a thought-provoking question about this topic which you have made up beforehand. You'll begin this procedure again with the next section.

The key to a deeper, more interesting and helpful discussion is having good questions prepared. These should challenge the group to look more closely at the subject and Scripture passage you are discussing.

This leader's material includes suggested discussion questions for each chapter in this book. However, you will probably want to write some of your own as well, so make a list before each group meeting. Write as many as you can think of. Having a good supply to choose from will help you quickly launch the discussion, and keep it going in the right direction.

These guidelines will also help:

Asking questions

1. Make sure your questions are simple and conversational.
2. Don't be afraid of silence after asking a question. Give everyone time to think.
3. Ask only one question at a time.
4. Don't ask questions which can be answered yes or no. This hinders discussion. Try beginning all your questions with "who," "what," "where," "when," "why," or "how."
5. A "What do you think?" question can help keep the discussion from seeming pressured or unnatural, since there is no such thing as a wrong answer to such a question. The person answering has freedom to simply give his viewpoint.

Other discussion
1. Remember that the Scriptures are the source of truth. Often you may want to look up together and read aloud the verses listed for the study questions as you discuss your answers.
2. Summarize frequently. Help the group see the direction of the discussion.
3. Allow time for adequate discussion on the application questions in each chapter. Your goal in Bible study is not, of course, to have something to discuss, but to change your life.
4. Allow adequate discussion also of the suggested family projects. Talk about how these can be adapted and implemented by everyone in the group.

General reminders
1. Your own attitude is a key factor in the group's enthusiasm. Develop a genuine interest in each person's remarks, and expect to learn from them.
2. Concentrate on developing acceptance and concern in the group. Avoid a businesslike atmosphere.
3. Participate in the discussion as a member of the group. Don't be either a lecturer or a silent observer.
4. You may want to begin each session by reviewing memorized Scripture, and then discussing progress made in the previous week on applications and family projects.
5. Your total discussion time should probably not exceed ninety minutes, and one hour might be best. Start and end on time. Remember, too, to close in group prayer.

You'll want to review these lists often.

AFTER
THE DISCUSSION

Use these self-evaluation questions after each session to help you improve your leadership the next time:
1. Did you discuss the major points in the chapter?
2. Did you have enough prepared questions to properly guide the discussion?

3. Did you know your material thoroughly enough to have freedom in leading?
4. Did you keep the discussion from wandering?
5. Did everyone participate in the discussion?
6. Was the discussion practical?
7. Did you begin and end on time?

Chapter 1

THE CHURCH AND THE FAMILY

OVERVIEW	OBJECTIVE
a. The Church—God's family b. Contributing to God's family c. The meaning of fellowship d. A model church e. The Church's impact on the world f. Application	To have each group member understand more deeply the value of other Christians to his life and to evaluate his family's church involvement.

For this session, and in later weeks, you may want to read the chapter objective and overview aloud to the group. This can help them see the overall focus of the chapter as they begin their discussion. You may also want to review these at the end of the discussion.

These questions from the study may promote the best discussion in your group as you share with each other your answers to them:

2, 4, 6, 7, 11, 12, 15, 19, 21, 24, and 25.

Each chapter in the study material includes application questions. These are designed to help a person apply a biblical truth to his life in a practical way. Since the written answers for these questions are personal, group members need to have the freedom *not* to share their

81

answers when you are discussing these questions. On the other hand, don't skip over the questions entirely, since the most beneficial discussion you can have is about how the Scriptures actually affect your day-to-day life.

A good way to stimulate discussion on an application question is to say something like, "Would any of you like to share with us your answer to Question 14?" or, "What did you learn about yourself (or your family) from Question 14?"

(In Chapter 1, Questions 14, 16, and 26 are application questions.)

Remember to discuss also the suggested family projects. You may want someone to read aloud the instructions. Then discuss how the projects can be used and adapted in each family represented in your group.

You could also have various group members read aloud the material on "How to Contribute to Your Church" (page 19), and discuss it point by point.

FOR FURTHER DISCUSSION

These questions can help you stimulate further discussion on some of the questions in this chapter:

For *Question 2:* Who makes up the Church?

Question 3: What does it mean to you that each member of Christ's Body belongs to each other?

Question 4: If a person has too low an estimate of his importance in the Body of Christ, what could he learn from this passage?

If a person has too high an estimate of his importance in the Body of Christ, what could he learn from this passage?

Question 7: What are the most important reasons to you why Christians need each other?

Question 8: Why are church leaders important?

Question 9 (Galatians 6:6): From whom do we receive instruction in the Word?

Question 13: Was the fellowship experience of the Christians in Acts different from what we experience today?

Questions 15-16: What to you is the greatest hindrance to experiencing true fellowship?

Questions 17-21: What most impressed you about the church in Thessalonica?

Question 18: Is your local church a model for others, as the Thessalonian church was?

Question 19: How can churches today have a worldwide impact?

Question 20: What is the importance in a church today of a proper acceptance of God's Word?
Is this being done in your church?

Question 22: What is the source of true love and unity in the Church?

Question 24 (Hebrews 10:24-25): How can we truly encourage someone?

Chapter 2

INFLUENCING NON-CHRISTIANS

OVERVIEW	OBJECTIVE
a. Salt, light, and fragrance b. Jesus' example c. Being in the world d. Application	To understand how important it is for Christians to be involved with non-Christians.

These questions from the study may promote the best discussion in your group:
1, 2, 3, 5, 6, 7, 8, 11, 13, 15, 17, and 18.

Remember also to discuss the application question (19) and the suggested family project.

At one or two points in the discussion you may find it appropriate to have a few moments of group prayer about a specific aspect of the study, such as recognizing opportunities to be involved in a loving way with non-Christians.

FOR FURTHER DISCUSSION

For *Question 4:* How does it detract from God's glory when Christians are complaining or involved in sinful desires?

Question 6: How can we increase glory to God through living a good life?

Question 8: Why do you think *fragrance* is a good word to describe the influence Christians can have in the world?

Question 12: Why did Jesus associate with the kind of people religious leaders looked down upon?

Question 14: What do you think Paul meant by saying he was a "slave to everyone"?

Question 15: How does your freedom in Christ allow you to truly serve others?

Question 16: What impressed you most in Jesus' prayer for His disciples?

Question 17: What keeps us from being "*of* the world"?

Chapter 3

VALUES AND CONDUCT

OVERVIEW	OBJECTIVE
a. Serving b. Priorities c. Possessions d. Being hospitable e. The importance of God's Word f. Application	To see more clearly some ways in which our lifestyle as Christians can be distinctive.

84

These questions from the study may promote the best discussion in your group:
3, 4, 5, 6, 9, 10, 13, 16, and 19.
Question 21 is an application question.

You may want to have some of the group members read aloud the material on "Ways Your Family Can Learn More from God's Word" (page 43). Perhaps some group members are already doing some of these things, and you can discuss the benefits or problems you are experiencing.

FOR FURTHER DISCUSSION

For *Question 1:* How did Jesus demonstrate servanthood in His life?

Question 2: Why is it often hard for us to serve others? When is it easiest to serve others?

Question 5: What evidences of these things do you see in your own family?

Question 6: How do you think prayer brings about peace and freedom from worry?

Question 7: Since the family is so important in God's eyes, how does that affect your view of your family responsibilities?

Question 8: Why must our relationship with Christ have priority over our family relationships?

Question 10: What is the contrast between the way people normally view possessions, and the Bible's teaching on possessions?

Question 11: How can the love of money be effectively overcome?

Question 15: What principles for hospitality did you observe in this passage?

Question 19: Why do you personally feel obeying the Scriptures is important for your family?

Question 20: What is the relationship between loving God and obeying His commands?
Is obedience the most important aspect of loving God?

85

Chapter 4

THE FAMILY AND WORK

OVERVIEW	OBJECTIVE
a. Old Testament principles and examples b. New Testament principles and examples c. Application	To learn how to enjoy our jobs and to work according to biblical guidelines.

These questions from the study may promote the best discussion in your group:
   4, 5, 6, 12, 15, 16, 18, 19, 22, 23, 24, and 25.
   Question 26 is an application question.

FOR FURTHER DISCUSSION

For *Question 1:* Why do you think God gave Adam this responsibility?

Question 4: How does this commandment show that God expects us to work?

Question 5: What most impressed you about the wife in Proverbs 31?

Question 6: Do you think craftsmanship and creativity among people today are gifts from God?

Question 7: What confidence do you think Joshua had in carrying out his duty?

Question 12: What are some examples of how God is at work today?

Question 14: What are some New Testament examples of how Jesus did everything well?

Question 16: What did Jesus' work on earth include?

Question 19: Why do you think hard work is important?

Question 22: What does it mean to you to work wholeheartedly?

Chapter 5

REACHING OUT

OVERVIEW	OBJECTIVE
a. Sent by God b. Who should we reach? c. Application	To understand how evangelistic outreach for a family is an ongoing process.

These questions from the study may promote the best discussion in your group:
3, 4, 5, 7, 8, 13, 14, and 16.

Remember also to discuss the application question (17) and the suggested family project.

You may also want someone to read aloud the paragraph following Question 14.

FOR FURTHER DISCUSSION

For *Question 2:* What do you think are the implications for His disciples of these words Jesus spoke?

Question 3: Why is it necessary for people to be sent to preach the Gospel?

How should these people be sent?

Question 4: How do you think the disciples might have reacted mentally to this statement from Jesus?

Question 6: What impressed you most about Paul's outreach for men?

Question 7: How prepared should we be to talk with others about the hope we have?

Question 8: What lessons did you learn from this passage in Acts?

Question 12: How could this incident be related to situations in the world today?

Question 14: What helps make non-Christians comfortable in our presence?

87

Chapter 6

OUR MESSAGE

OVERVIEW	OBJECTIVE
a. The source of the message b. God's plan of salvation c. Application	To know and be able to discuss with non-Christians the essential elements of the Gospel of Jesus Christ.

These questions may promote the best discussion in your group:
1, 3, 5, 6, 8, 9, 11, 12, 14, 15, 17, and 19.
Questions 18 and 20 are application questions.

FOR FURTHER DISCUSSION

For *Question 1:* What is the relationship between faith and hearing or reading the Scriptures?

Question 3: What lesson can you learn from these three passages?

Question 4: How does the Holy Spirit do these things?

Question 5: How do the Holy Spirit, the Bible, and Christians work together in bringing others to belief in Christ?

Question 7: Why are each of these ingredients important?

Question 8: What for you is the personal significance of Christ's resurrection?

Question 11: How would you explain why so many refuse to believe in Christ after hearing the Gospel?

Question 12: How can we demonstrate God's power in our witness to others?

Question 14: What lessons can we learn from the situation described in Acts 15?

SUGGESTED READING

Barclay, William. *Ethics in a Permissive Society.*
New York: Harper and Row, 1972.

Bridges, Jerry. *The Pursuit of Holiness.* NavPress,
1978.

Lloyd-Jones, D. Martin. *Life in the Spirit in Mar-
riage, Home, and Work.* Grand Rapids, Michigan:
Baker Book House, 1975.

Mains, Karen. *Open Heart, Open Home.* Wheaton,
Illinois: Tyndale House, 1976.

Peabody, Larry. *Secular Work Is Full-time Service.*
Philadelphia: Christian Literature Crusade, 1974.

Sider, Ronald. *Rich Christians in an Age of Hunger.*
Downers Grove, Illinois: InterVarsity Press, 1977.

White, Jerry. *Honesty, Morality, and Conscience.*
NavPress, 1978.

White, Jerry and Mary. *Your Job—Survival or
Satisfaction.* Grand Rapids, Michigan: Zondervan
Publishing House, 1977.